Tom and Bella have made a sandcastle on the beach. They have put sandpies round it.

Tom is digging a moat round the sandcastle. Bella is digging a channel to the sea.

'Tom, look! The sea has reached my channel,' says Bella. 'The water is coming down it.'

'Here it comes,' says Tom.
'Look! The sea is filling the
moat with water.'

Tom and Bella jump up and down. They are very happy with the sandcastle and the moat.

Oh no! The water has reached the sandpies. Oh no! They are collapsing into the sea.

Oh no! The sandcastle is falling down too. The sea is washing the sandcastle away.

The sandcastle has gone. The sea has covered it all. Tom and Bella have fun in the water.